The TV

THE TURBUL

OF

TYKE TILER

Gene Kemp

Dramatised by
Richard Callanan
Follow-up activities by
Ray Speakman

HEINEMANN
SPOTLIGHTS

Heinemann Educational Books

Heinemann Educational Books Ltd
22 Bedford Square, London WC1B 3HH

LONDON   EDINBURGH   MELBOURNE   AUCKLAND
SINGAPORE   KUALA LUMPUR   NEW DELHI
NAIROBI   JOHANNESBURG   IBADAN
KINGSTON   PORTSMOUTH (NH)

ISBN 435 23003 4

The cover photograph is from the Yorkshire Television
production of THE TURBULENT TERM OF TYKE TILER and
shows 'Tyke' Curtis as Tyke and Robert Rumsby as Danny.

Typeset by Latimer Trend & Company Ltd, Plymouth
Printed and bound in Great Britain by
J. W. Arrowsmith, Bristol and London

CONTENTS

INTRODUCTION TO THE TEACHER

The Turbulent Term of Tyke Tiler is an adaptation for television by Richard Callanan of Gene Kemp's novel of the same name. The eight episodes are presented here exactly as they were broadcast, and like the novel, each episode is full of incident, humour and insight. As such they will prove an entertaining classroom read and a stimulating source of discussion and writing for younger secondary school pupils.

It goes without saying that teachers of English will devise activities arising out of a reading of these scripts which will best suit the abilities and needs of the pupils with whom they are used. Thus the suggestions presented at the end of each episode and at the end of the eight episodes are intended very much as 'suggestions' – they are not the only way to respond to the script in terms of style or quantity – the teacher in the classroom will best know that.

The central intention behind the follow-up activities is to encourage a creative response to Richard Callanan's drama, and to promote a careful, thoughtful reading of the text. Each episode is followed by three sections – 'Keeping Track' which might be used for discussion immediately after reading each episode, for written comprehension, or for shaping a 'reading journal'; 'A Closer Look' suggests discussion, writing and drama arising out of one or more of the main incidents in each episode; 'Explorations' puts forward some ideas which might be used to widen the situations or issues raised by the episode and encourage a creative, more personal response. The short section at the end, 'Afterwords', suggests a more detailed response to the story.

The teacher will see that a number of the questions asked of the pupils, and some of the activities suggested, are quite clearly intended as an introduction to the sort of work pupils will encounter later on in the secondary school. In particular, there is encouragement to look closely at, and write about, characters – what sort of people they are, how what they say (and how they say it) can reveal their characters, and how they change during the course of the narrative. There is also some attention given to themes and to the writer's technique.

Further to this, teachers should find it possible to shape and re-arrange some of this material to suit their own, and their pupils', needs. For instance, an extended comprehension could quite easily be assembled using selected questions from the 'Keeping Track' section at the end of each episode; similarly, a detailed character study might be put together by listing separately the appropriate questions. However the teacher uses the scripts, whether for short term reading, or long-term examination, they should prove a rich source for classroom activity.

Reading the Scripts in the Classroom

In general terms. *The Turbulent Term of Tyke Tiler* is an extremely accessible play for pupils (of a wide ability range) to read out loud in the classroom. The economy of the writing, as well as its humour, should encourage most pupils to approach the sometimes daunting prospect of a public reading with enthusiasm. However, the follow-ing notes on the characters (and what is required of the reader) should help the teacher to organise an effective and enjoyable reading of the play.

Tyke: appears in every scene – the events are seen from her point of view. Most of her speeches, however, are short and easy to read. She needs to be cast very carefully for a reading because Tyke is a girl, but we do not fully realise this until the end of the last episode.
Danny: like Tyke, Danny is in a large number of scenes. His lines however, are short and straightforward. (Nevertheless, the part requires a reader who can concentrate and not lose their place.)
The Headteacher: although he only appears in a limited number of scenes, I suspect this part would prove difficult for a pupil to read –

his language, and sense of humour, is adult and therefore probably best read by the teacher.

Mrs Somers: even fewer scenes than the Headteacher, but some long speeches. Requires a fluent reader.

The other adults (Mr Merchant, Miss Honeywell, Mr and Mrs Tiler): none of these are particularly difficult reads – although Mr Merchant does have one or two long speeches.

The other children: (Kneeshaw, Pitt, Linda): very straightforward.

Altogether, teachers should find that the play comes to life easily in the classroom and the pupils will find the narrative and the dialogue engrossing. It is also particularly appropriate for recording on tape – or even on video.

Production

Throughout the notes which accompany the text I have largely assumed classroom reading and activity. The script would also be interesting to approach from the point of view of school production (using parts, or the whole text). With so many short scenes, an open stage approach would obviously be easiest – particularly if done in the round. Lighting and sound might be used to show passage of time, or change of setting. The only scene which might prove difficult is the clocktower incident in episode eight – and even this could well be managed as an off-stage piece of business.

THE CHARACTERS

TYKE TILER: According to the Head Tyke is 'a disobedient, under-educated, under-disciplined loud-mouthed ruffian.' Certainly Tyke is always getting into trouble but more often than not that's Danny's fault. This is one reason why Tyke is always considering: 'the unfairness of life. This is a very interesting subject, and one I spend some time on, especially at school, though there's a fair amount of injustice at home too.'

DANNY PRICE: Danny is considered 'thick' by most of his classmates and teachers. He comes from a poor family, his father is in prison, and he has taken to stealing and gets into endless trouble. He has been adopted by Tyke who is his only friend.

DAD: Tyke's Dad is an engine driver for British Rail and very involved with local politics. He's a friendly man who enjoys his children and can take a joke.

MUM: Mum is a night nurse at the hospital. 'I bet the patients daren't even die when she's there if she doesn't allow it,' says Tyke. Mum is very fond of Tyke but only wishes people would not use that 'terrible nickname'.

THE HEAD: The Head has been at Cricklepit School for years and years. He has seen it all before and, although he doesn't actually hate the job, he's looking forward to retirement when it comes.

MRS SOMERS: Most people would think that Mrs Somers doesn't like children very much. She is the Deputy Head and last year she taught Tyke. She is a strict teacher and believes that Tyke's manners and behaviour are in serious need of improvement.

'SIR': William Merchant is Tyke and Danny's class teacher. He's a relaxed kind of man and popular with the kids. Local history is his favourite subject and he has written a book about the school.

MISS HONEYWELL: Jenny Honeywell is a student teacher starting her career. She comes from a very posh background and it will take her a while to get used to the rough and tumble of Cricklepit School.

BERYL: Tyke's older sister, is very interested in pop music and her own appearance. She is now going out with Richard, her first serious boyfriend.

MARTIN KNEESHAW, KEVIN SIMMS, LINDA STOATWAY, IAN PITT: Classmates of Tyke and Danny. Kneeshaw and his sidekick Simms are Tyke and Danny's sworn enemies.

CRUMBLE: Tyke's spaniel.

EPISODE ONE

Scene 1

Small downstairs hall at Cricklepit Combined School. Classrooms lead directly off.

TYKE *and* DANNY *are coming out of a classroom.* TYKE *counts change into a tin labelled 'Staff Tea Money'.* DANNY *waves a ten-pound note in front of* TYKE, *who glares at him in exasperation.* TYKE *turns and walks determinedly away.*

DANNY: Tyke!

DANNY *follows* TYKE *and they meet up again at the other end of the hall.*

TYKE: Where didja get that, you nutter?
DANNY: Out of Bonfire's purse. She'd left it open. On the desk.
  So I took it. No one saw me, Tyke.
TYKE: Danny Price!

TYKE *shakes* DANNY *in exasperation. A door opens at the other end of the hall and in pour a very junior class in school play costumes.* TYKE *and* DANNY *exchange glances.* TYKE *snatches the ten-pound note and* DANNY *looks on dumbly as it is carefully hidden up* TYKE'S *jumper.*

Scene 2

Top of school stairs. TYKE *is rushing up from below.* DANNY *is trying to keep up.*

TYKE: Don't you see? Don't you understand?
DANNY: Why you all mad, Tyke? Don't be mad at me, Tyke.

TYKE *is silent.*

DANNY: I got it for you. I want you to have half of it. You can buy anything you like, Tyke.

DANNY *pulls at* TYKE's *arm, but* TYKE *shakes him off.*

TYKE: Get knotted.
DANNY: Tyke. Tyke?

But TYKE *has gone into their classroom.*

Scene 3
School classroom. 4M's teacher is not present. Two girls are dancing in a corner, showing off. A couple of boys are fighting. MARTIN KNEESHAW *is standing on a desk giving them orders.*

KNEESHAW: C'mon, Kevin! Well, kick him. Go on!

TYKE *walks in followed by* DANNY, KNEESHAW *greets them.*

KNEESHAW: Look who's come back to us – the zoo-keeper, complete with monkey.
TYKE *(very direct)*: You shut your face, Martin Kneeshaw, or you'll be swallowing teeth for a month.

TYKE *turns away and joins* DANNY *at the back of the class. The uproar from the other kids continues.*

TYKE: Listen, Danny. Don't you understand? You can't spend it, because they'll ask you where you got it from, and they won't believe what you say and then they'll want to ask your Mum, and then you'll be for it.

DANNY *looks very sad.*

TYKE: It's no use, Danny boyo. You can't keep it.

DANNY: I didn't think.

TYKE: You never do, do you? Now, go and give it back to Bonfire.

DANNY: I can't do that. You know the row I got into last time.

TYKE: What are we going to do with it, then? Play Monopoly with it? Stick it up on the wall?

DANNY: Hide it and put it back later.

TYKE: You must be joking!

DANNY: Please, Tyke. You do it. You're clever. You can do anything.

TYKE: Gee, thanks.

DANNY: Oh go on, Tyke, please.

TYKE *(fed up with Danny but thinking hard)*: Oh, get stuffed, Danny Price. Any minute now they'll start screaming 'Stop Thief' all around the school . . .

    TYKE *breaks off as* SIR *comes in.*

SIR: What's all this row about? Come on, I expect some decent work from you lot before the end of the day. Please get off the floor, Kevin, there's enough litter about.

TYKE *(with hand raised)*: Sir?

SIR: Yes, Tyke?

TYKE: Can I take the tea money to the office, please, Sir?

SIR: Yes, Tyke.

    Afraid that it might be slipping, TYKE *tries to hold the hidden ten-pound note in place.*

SIR: Anything the matter?

TYKE: Nothing, Sir.

SIR: You look a bit green. Got a pain?

TYKE *(rushing out)*: No, Sir.

    TYKE *goes.*

SIR: Right then. To work!

Scene 4

Along one wall of large school hall.

TYKE *approaches a rubbish bin and starts to take out the ten-pound note. The important thing is to get rid of it — if only for the time being. There seems to be no-one about but suddenly a door opens, footsteps approach and there stands* MRS SOMERS, *Deputy Head and no friend of* TYKE's.

MRS SOMERS: What are you doing out here?

TYKE: Taking tea money.

MRS SOMERS: Don't mumble, child. And look up when a member of staff speaks to you.

TYKE: Yes, Miss.

MRS SOMERS: And another thing. I still hear other children calling you 'Tyke'. It's a name from the gutter, child. You have a perfectly good name haven't you?

TYKE: Yes, Miss.

MRS SOMERS: You haven't forgotten it, have you?

TYKE: No, Miss.

MRS SOMERS: Well use it. Now run along. *(Turns back the way she came.)*

MRS SOMERS *sweeps off.* TYKE *makes an appalling monster face after her. As* MRS SOMERS *turns back,* TYKE *tries to wipe the face off quickly.*

MRS SOMERS: Well, move!

TYKE *moves off.*

Scene 5

Storeroom with trap-door to attic store room. TYKE *expertly and with no fear climbs up partitions or stores to push open attic door and climbs in.*

Scene 6
Dark attic store room. TYKE *turns on a low-wattage bulb to reveal stored clutter. Hanging on the wall is a picture of a sailor pointing out to sea with Sir Walter Raleigh. Swiftly* TYKE *puts the ten-pound note behind the picture and switches off the light.*

Scene 7
School classroom. SIR, *the* HEAD *and* MRS SOMERS *stand in front of the class.* DANNY *is very attentive.*

HEAD: Would anyone like to own up now, to save trouble and unpleasantness later?

    Silence. Door opens and in walks TYKE.

TYKE: 'Scuse me, Sir.

    MRS SOMERS *glares at* TYKE *who goes to sit beside* DANNY.

HEAD *(to Sir)*: If the money has not been recovered by the time I've seen all the classes, then I'll send a message to you that all desks, bags, pockets and coats are to be searched. No-one will be allowed home until everything has been checked.

    THE HEAD *and* MRS SOMERS *leave. There is general uproar.*

KNEESHAW: Don't see why we should stay in. 'Tisn't fair.
SIMMS: Betcha it was someone in her own class. How could it be one of us?
LINDA: My Mum says its a temptation to others to leave your money lying about.
KNEESHAW: Your Mum is an old boot.
SIR: Quiet please and get back to your work. This is all we needed.

    THE CLASS *settles down.* DANNY *is colouring a bird with a blue felt-tip pen.*

TYKE: What's that? A kingfisher?
DANNY: No, a robin.
TYKE: They're brown and red, twit.
DANNY: I like it blue.
TYKE *(quieter)*: It's OK. I got rid of it.
DANNY: What? What you got rid of, Tyke?

   TYKE *moves as if to hit him.*

DANNY: Oh yes. I know. The ten ...
TYKE: Shut up you halfwit!
SIR: Leave Danny alone. He was working well till you disturbed
   him, Tyke.

Scene 8

*Outside the school. TYKE and DANNY are leaving through the main
gates. Other children also going home. DANNY, as usual, just behind
TYKE. TYKE is pausing, as if to cross road.*

DANNY *(pleased)*: They couldn't find the tenner on anyone,
   could they?
TYKE: How could they find it, dopey, when I'd hidden it? And
   what will we do when they have the police in on Monday?
DANNY *(worried and needing help)*: Tyke, can I come round to
   your house after tea?
TYKE: Don't bother. I don't care if you drop dead, Danny Price.

   TYKE *crosses the road and walks on home without looking back.*
   DANNY *is left alone and unhappy.*

Scene 9

*The lounge in TYKE's home. The room is furnished simply and
comfortably. TYKE is lounging on the sofa taking only a little interest in
an old comic. There's a click as the front door opens, TYKE jumps up
quietly, hides behind the door and jumps on the man who comes in.
It's DAD.*

DAD: You crazy fool. Are you trying to flatten me?

They wrestle on the floor. DAD *gets the upper hand.*

DAD: Submit.
TYKE: I submit. Dad?
DAD: Yeah.
TYKE: Dad, would teachers miss ten pounds if they lost it?
DAD: Yes. Now bed. The day's long enough without you at the
end of it, horrible.

TYKE, *going out the door takes a final playful swipe at* DAD.

DAD: Good night, Tyke.

TYKE *is already on the stairs.*

TYKE: 'Night, Dad.

TYKE's *gone.* DAD *shuts the lounge door and grins.*

Scene 10
TYKE's *bedroom.* TYKE *is sitting on the bed with the family pet,*
CRUMBLE, *a blue roan cocker spaniel.*

TYKE: Crumble, I think I know what I have to do on Monday.

Scene 11
The school. Room with trap-door to attic. TYKE *enters the room*
cautiously and climbs up to the attic door.

Scene 12
Attic store-room. TYKE *climbs in. Turns on light, looks around. The*
painting of Raleigh is no longer there.

TYKE *(very quietly, disbelieving)*: It's gone!

MUSIC

EPISODE ONE

Keeping Track

1 Why does Danny steal the money?
2 How does Tyke feel about Danny's crime? How does Tyke express those feelings?
3 What does Danny's way of talking tell you about him? Give examples of the way he speaks.
4 What is Kneeshaw doing when he first appears in the episode? What does this tell you about him?
5 What does Kneeshaw mean when he calls Tyke a 'zoo-keeper'?
6 What are Mrs Soames and Sir like? Find a sentence in one of their speeches which you think illustrates each of their characters.
7 Where does Tyke hide the ten-pound note?
8 When Tyke returns after hiding the money, Danny has forgotten what Tyke has been doing. What does this tell you about Danny?
9 Tyke says, 'I don't care if you drop dead, Danny Price.' How do you know that this *doesn't* mean that Tyke is cruel to Danny?
10 Describe what happens at the end of Episode One. How is the writer encouraging you to keep reading (or watching)?

A Closer Look

1 Discuss the incident of the stolen money. How do the teachers react? What do they say? What method do they seem to be using to recover the money?
2 Imagine you are a member of that class and you *know* who took the money. Write a letter to your favourite magazine explaining what has happened and asking what you should do about it.

3 Write the reply *from* the magazine in which advice is offered.

Explorations

Imagine that your mother has given you a ten–pound note to pay for a school trip (or to buy something you need on the way home from school, or to pay a bill for her – like the newspaper shop). You take the money to school and it is stolen. Explore this situation in one of the following ways:

(a) Write the story of what happens – how you try to find the money, who you tell at school, what happens, how you tell your mother about it, what she says, how you feel throughout all this – and so on.

or

(b) Act out (or write the scene) in which you tell your mother what has happened.

or

(c) Imagine that a friend of yours knows who took the money but is unwilling to reveal who it was. Act or write the scene in which you try to talk the friend into telling you. (The friend must have reasons for not telling – are they frightened to tell? Are they loyal to the thief? Do they not approve of 'grassing'?) How would you answer these reasons?

EPISODE TWO

Scene 1

School playground. The children are waiting to enter the school.
DANNY is wandering around with a newspaper parcel under his arm.
Eventually he finds a worried TYKE slipping out of a side-door in the school.

DANNY: Guess what I got, Tyke.

TYKE: Fish and chips. They'll love you in Assembly.

DANNY: It ain't fish and chips. The shops don't open till twelve. Guess again.

He grins and unwraps the newspaper, dropping it everywhere.

DANNY: It's a bone. A bone for your dog, Crumble.

TYKE turns on a very junior kid.

TYKE: Pick that newspaper up, you. And put it in the bin.

Reluctantly the kid obeys. TYKE eyes the huge bone.

TYKE: What have you done, Danny? Killed a brontosaurus?

DANNY: It's a marrow bone, Tyke.

TYKE: And just where am I supposed to keep that, all day? Along with the tenner that's disappeared?

DANNY: What?

TYKE: Yeh, the tenner you stole, it's missing. I put it behind an old painting in the store and the painting's gone, vanished.

DANNY stares blankly, not sure what this will mean. A whistle blows and they file into the school.

Scene 2

School hall with Assembly in progress. All are singing 'One More Step along the Road I Go'. At the front are the HEAD, SIR, MRS SOMERS and another teacher playing the piano. TYKE is gazing round but suddenly focusses on the missing painting of Raleigh now displayed on an easel for all to see. Obviously the tenner has been found. TYKE feels terrible and fervently joins in the singing.

Beside TYKE, DANNY takes from his pocket a black and white piebald mouse which he strokes lovingly. He then places it in the hair of LINDA STOATWAY who stands in front of him. She reacts jumping forward and into another child. Like nine-pins each child falls into the next until a child at the front falls onto the piano keyboard. Loud discord, the hymn stops.

The mouse now runs towards MRS SOMERS who screams and climbs the first two rungs of the wall bars. SIR does a flying tackle to catch the mouse but ends in an embarrassed heap at MRS SOMERS' feet. Her glare implies he's to blame.

Several children are now running after the mouse but the HEAD swiftly and calmly scoops it up and returns to his place. Things quieten down. MRS SOMERS and SIR recover their dignity. The HEAD waits for absolute silence. You can hear a mouse squeak.

HEAD: I should like the owner of this little fellow to come to my room at playtime.

Scene 3

School classroom. TYKE is working on a Duodecahedron. SIR is at the door talking to a child from another class.

SIR: Tyke!

   TYKE looks up unhappily.

SIR *(not unkindly)*: The Head wants to see you in his room. Now.

   It's a long walk to the door. TYKE goes out.

Scene 4
The Head's office. The HEAD is sitting at his desk going through papers. There's a knock on the door.

HEAD: *(not looking up)*: Come in.

 TYKE enters reluctantly. Eventually the HEAD looks up, says nothing then takes the ten-pound note out of his pocket and holds it towards TYKE.

HEAD: Have you seen this before?

 Silence.

TYKE: I didn't steal it.
HEAD: You did not answer my question. Have you seen it before?

 Silence.

HEAD: Speak up, Tyke. Tell me what you know.
TYKE: There's nothing to tell. Only I didn't take it.
HEAD: Tyke, I know you to be a disobedient, under-educated, under-disciplined, loud-mouthed ruffian but I have known you for some seven or eight years and I have not hitherto noted any special tendency towards mendacity.
TYKE: No, Sir.
HEAD: What do you mean. 'No, Sir'?
TYKE: I don't know what you mean.
HEAD: I don't think you're a liar.

 The HEAD rises, crosses left and waters a plant on the windowsill with a tea-pot.

HEAD: You see when the caretaker found the ten-pound note I thought of you, Tyke. Of all the pupils I have taught over the years, the only two capable of getting into that loft without a ladder, are your brother Stanley, now happily removed to another establishment and yourself. What have you got to say?

Silence. The HEAD *continues very quietly.*

HEAD: Come, come, tell me about it. You didn't steal it, but you did put it in the loft, didn't you?

TYKE *stares at the floor.*

TYKE: Yes.
HEAD: Good. Now we're getting somewhere.

HEAD *turns on* TYKE *suddenly.*

HEAD: What made you hide that money for Danny Price?

TYKE *doesn't know what to say. In the silence there is a knock at the door which both ignore.*

HEAD: Well?

DANNY *barges in, spluttering incoherently.*

DANNY: Fatty is not Tyke's mouse. Fatty is my mouse.
HEAD: Now, Danny, let's take it slowly, shall we, one word at a time?
TYKE: Danny says that it wasn't my mouse, it was his.
DANNY: Daddy!

DANNY *has seen his pet piebald mouse in a goldfish bowl on the head's desk.*

TYKE: He means 'Fatty'. That's the mouse's name.

The HEAD *has lost his intensity, he's more astonished than angry. He sits.*

HEAD: Do you mean to tell me, Daniel Price, that you're responsible for that — that circus in the hall this morning — as well as stealing a large sum of money from a teacher?
DANNY *(incoherently)*: I didn't mean to take her money.
HEAD: What on earth is he saying?
TYKE: He didn't mean to make Miss Bonn cry. He likes her, you see. And he isn't speaking very well just now because he's upset.

TYKE: Please, Sir.

HEAD: Yes, Tyke.

TYKE: He didn't mean to take the money. It was only because it was there in front of him. And I hid it in the loft so that I could put it back when things had gone quiet. But it all went wrong.

DANNY: Yes, Sir.

The HEAD *examines each of them in turn.*

HEAD: I see. Well. It seems we had better start at the beginning. Go and fetch Miss Bonn and Mr Merchant for me. This is going to take some time.

Scene 5

Corner of a cloakroom in school. MRS SOMERS *is peering with some disgust into a shoe-bag.* LINDA *is looking on smugly.*

MRS SOMERS: Yes, Linda. Today has been full of surprises. You did right to tell me.

Scene 6

School corridor outside HEAD'*s office.* TYKE *is being seen out of the office by the* HEAD *who is sealing an envelope which he then hands to* TYKE.

HEAD: And tomorrow, Tyke, I'd like to see a response to this letter from your parents. They have a right to know what you get up to at school. All right?

TYKE: Yes, Sir.

HEAD: And try to keep out of trouble, Tyke. The consequences next time might be much more serious.

TYKE *(still subdued)*: Yes, Sir. Thank you, Sir.

The HEAD *goes back into his office closing the door.* TYKE, *visibly relieved, sets off down the corridor doing three cartwheels but ends up at the feet of* MRS SOMERS *who has rounded the corner.*

MRS SOMERS: I don't believe it! Will you ever learn any decorum? You, child, must stay in after school and write out 200 times, 'I must not behave like an international gymnast in the corridor'. And another thing. What's this horrid object doing in your shoe-bag?

MRS SOMERS *removes the mammoth marrow bone from the bag with great disgust.*

MRS SOMERS: You mustn't bring such things to school, you know. Now take it away. And bring me those lines tomorrow morning, first thing.

MRS SOMERS *strides off.* TYKE *is left dejected only to be greeted by an excessively cheery* DANNY.

DANNY: Tyke! D'ya know what's happened?
TYKE: Oh, it's you.
DANNY: In the end Miss Bonn wasn't cross at all. She started crying and saying how sorry she was. And she's invited me home to her house for tea! She says we can get cream buns on the way.
TYKE: That's great, that is. You steal ten pounds and get a cream tea. I try to help and I get detention and a letter home. That's what I call justice.
DANNY *(missing the irony)*: Is it?

TYKE *turns away in disgust.*

MUSIC

EPISODE TWO

Keeping Track

1 Danny brings to school a bone for Tyke's dog, Crumble. What makes him do this?

2 What is Tyke's reaction the the gift? What difficulties did Danny not think of in bringing the bone to school?

3 Can you find any evidence to support the view that Mrs Somers treats other teachers in the same way as she treats the children of the school?

4 What happens with Danny's mouse? Is Danny trying to cause trouble with his mouse? Can you see any connection between the incident with the mouse and the present Danny gives to Tyke at the beginning of the episode? What is the writer emphasising about Danny through these two incidents?

5 When Tyke is interviewed by the Headteacher how does Tyke avoid actually telling lies?

6 How does the Headteacher know that Tyke has hidden the money?

7 Why does Tyke have to 'interpret' for Danny when Danny is being interviewed by the Headteacher?

8 Once he is sure of the truth, the Headteacher chooses to deal with the theft in a particular way. How?

9 Why does Miss Bonn cry when she learns the truth?

10 In the very last line of the episode the word 'irony' is used in a stage direction. Look at Tyke's speech before this direction. What does the word 'irony' mean do you think? Why does Danny miss this irony?

A Closer Look

1 Discuss the way in which the Headteacher deals with the theft and Tyke's part in it. Is he too 'soft'? Do you think he should have been more severe?

2 Imagine you are the Headteacher and you have to write a report about what happened, and how you dealt with it, for the school Governors. Outline the events and say why you acted as you did when the 'thieves' were discovered.

3 Write a speech for Mrs Somers in which she forcibly tells the Headteacher that he should have been more severe. Say what she would have done and give her reasons. Before you start, look closely at the way she speaks and see if you can make your speech sound like her.

Explorations

Imagine that your parents receive a letter from the Headteacher of your school telling them that you have done something wrong in school, (you have set the fire alarm off or you have broken an item of expensive equipment or you are not working hard enough, for instance). Explore this situation in one of the following ways:

(a) Write the story of what happens – from the time the letter arrives at your house. You could perhaps include a visit by your parents to the school to discuss the matter with the Headteacher.
or

(b) Act or write the breakfast table scene when the letter is opened.
or

(c) Act or write the interview between your parents and the Headteacher.

EPISODE THREE

Scene 1

Exterior of old castle. SIR is giving a history lesson on a school outing. 4M are very involved. Beside them they have a huge bag of their class-made helmets, swords and battle-axes.

SIR *(in mid-flow)*: The people made the city walls and gates even stronger. They were determined not to give in, but William himself appeared before the city gates and gave orders for one of the hostages to be blinded in front of the people.

DANNY: Ooerh. 'Ow 'orrible.

TYKE: Did he stick a hot iron in the fellow's eye?

SIR: No, it was gouged out.

Several expressions of disgust.

SIR: They were cruel times. But guess what happened next?

DANNY: You tell us, Sir.

SIR: A most uncivilised citizen, probably an ancestor of yours, Pitt, made a rude gesture back at William.

PITT *(out of vision)*: Like this, you mean, Sir?

SIR: Don't all do one or we'll be turned out.

KNEESHAW: Bet old William was mad, Sir.

SIR: Yes, indeed, he was mad. And so, for eighteen days he surrounded the city and besieged it.

PITT: Who won?

KNEESHAW: We did, of course.

SIR: In the end neither side won. William agreed to an honourable surrender and swore on the sacred books in the cathedral that he wouldn't harm the people or impose heavy taxes.

KNEESHAW: We won. Hurray!
SIR: In a way. But William changed the countr̩

> SIR *stands quietly for a moment, his face serious.*

DANNY: Please, can we act the battle?
SIR: Yes, get your clobber. Kneeshaw, pick a side. And let me see, yes, Tyke, you pick a side.

> *Watching from a distance, a TRAMP shakes his head at today's youth and takes another swig from his bottle of cider.*

Scene 2
Exterior or courtyard of old castle. The battle. TYKE and the ENGLISH by the castle wall, KNEESHAW and the NORMANS besieging them. Much pulling of faces.

TYKE: Right, then. Charge.

> *Shouts and howls as the ENGLISH advance. TYKE goes straight for KNEESHAW.*

KNEESHAW: Fight for Kneeshaw!
TYKE: No, fight for Tiler, and England!
SIR: Careful!

> TYKE *bashes KNEESHAW on the helmet, he staggers back and falls over a tree root. TYKE falls on him. Armour tangles, helmets fall off. TYKE grabs him by the hair and holds him down.*

TYKE: Submit.

> SIR *blows his whistle and TYKE and KNEESHAW stop fighting.*

SIR: OK, OK. Battle's over. Let's get back to school.

Scene 3
Pavement of city street. 4M are returning to school, tramping heavily on the pavement and chanting.

Geezer,

his wife with a lemon squeezer.

repeating this. At the back, SIR *is beside* TYKE.

SIR: How's your father, Tyke? Is he standing for the Council
again, this year?

TYKE: Don't know, Sir.

SIR: Don't know? Where's your sense of civic responsibility?

TYKE: Don't know, Sir.

SIR: No, I suppose you wouldn't.

KNEESHAW *turns round from in front.*

KNEESHAW: My Dad is going to stand against Tyke's Dad in
the council election, Sir.

SIR: Is he really?

TYKE *has known nothing of this.*

KNEESHAW: Yeah. He says he's going to beat him too.

KNEESHAW *and* TYKE *exchange dirty looks.*

Scene 4
Kitchen/diner in Tyke's home. Tyke's MUM *is washing up.* DAD *is
drying.*

MUM *(calling)*: Tyke! Tyke!

TYKE *comes in.*

TYKE: Yeah?

MUM: Finish clearing the table, will you, love?

TYKE *sets about doing this.*

TYKE: Why is it always me? Where's Spud?

MUM: At football.

TYKE: And where's Beryl?

DAD: Canvassing.

TYKE: Huh!

DAD: Well, I have to win this election, don't I?

TYKE: Danny's coming around. We'll take Crumble for a walk.

DAD: Terrific. If you're going for a walk you can deliver some
leaflets.

TYKE: Oh, no.

DAD *reaches for a pile from a kitchen shelf.*

DAD: Come on. It's only a couple of streets. And there's twenty
pence.

Front door bell rings.

TYKE: Okay.

DAD: Thanks, Tyke.

TYKE *leaves the room.*

DAD *(calling after)*: And don't forget. Push those leaflets right into
the letter-boxes. *(to Mum)* We don't want the opposition
removing them, do we?

Scene 5

Bridge over stream in the city. TYKE, DANNY *and* CRUMBLE
approach bridge, lean over parapet. TYKE *is reading leaflet,* DANNY
inspecting stream.

TYKE: 'Your rent and your rates.' Huh!

DANNY: Nothin' interestin'. No skellintons. What's that?

TYKE: What? Where?

DANNY: Over there.

DANNY *jogs* TYKE's *arm. The election leaflets fall into the
water.*

TYKE: Now you've gone and done it!

DANNY: I'm sorry, Tyke.

TYKE: Oh well. I don't suppose anyone would have read it anyway. Come on.

TYKE *and* DANNY *walk on leaving the leaflets floating away.*

Scene 6

Exterior of old mill. TYKE *and* DANNY *have climbed a wall into the grounds of an old disused mill. They let* CRUMBLE *off the leash and* CRUMBLE *runs ahead.*

TYKE: They used to make paper here. Sir told us.

DANNY: Do you think we could get in, Tyke? I've never been inside it.

Old pieces of wood, doors, sheets of plywood, have been nailed roughly across the entrance. TYKE *and* DANNY *pull one piece away.* CRUMBLE *goes in and they follow.*

Scene 7

Inside the old mill which has high ceilings, dark beams, naked light bulbs, cobwebs, dust — echoes. There's a low rumbling sound of water rushing by, the old mill stream under the building. TYKE *and* DANNY *walk on tiptoe.* CRUMBLE *darts around.*

TYKE: Come back, Crumble!

TYKE *and* DANNY *follow* CRUMBLE *up a wooden staircase.*

TYKE: Look out, Danny! There's some broken floorboards here. Come back, Crumble!

DANNY: Tyke, let's go back.

TYKE: I just want a look and then I'll come.

DANNY: Do you think there's a ghost, Tyke?

TYKE: 'Course not.

DANNY: It looks ghosty. I don't like it, Tyke.

TYKE: Just this bit more.

> *There's a square kind of trap door in one of the walls.* CRUMBLE *noses it and it swings up. The roar of water increases.*

TYKE: No, Crumble!

> CRUMBLE *goes through, the door swings shut.* TYKE *dives through the door.*

Scene 8
Small attic type room in mill with several wooden boxes around, piles of old paper, sacks etc. TYKE *dives in, grabs* CRUMBLE, *cuddles him. Puts on his lead.* DANNY *looks in.*

TYKE: Let's go.

> TYKE, DANNY *and* CRUMBLE *leave.*

Scene 9
Street near TYKE's *house.* MARTIN KNEESHAW *is delivering leaflets into letter-boxes.* DANNY *and* TYKE *are walking along.*

TYKE: Don't tell anyone, Danny. It's gonna be our secret place.
DANNY: It scares me.
TYKE: Chicken.
DANNY: No, I ain't. I ain't scared of nothing but them ghosts in there.

> TYKE *spots* MARTIN KNEESHAW *on other side of road.*

TYKE: Hey, look who it is — William the conquered.
KNEESHAW: I've got better things to do than talk to you, Tyke Tiler.

> KNEESHAW *turns a corner and walks away smartish.*

TYKE: What's he been up to, then?

TYKE *sees a leaflet hanging half out of the nearest letter-box, removes it and reads it out.*

TYKE: 'My rent and rates policy by Grendon Kneeshaw.'

DANNY: What's got into you, Tyke?

TYKE: Oh, Danny, boyo, that stupid, nutborough, nittly Kneeshaw hasn't got a clue . . .

DANNY: What? What hasn't he got a clue about? Tell me what it says, Tyke.

TYKE: These are his father's election leaflets. He doesn't know that if you leave stuff like this lying around, the enemy will grab it. And we're the enemy. Come on, let's take all of Kneecheese's leaflets we can find.

TYKE *and* DANNY *run up the street removing leaflets from letter-boxes, and doorsteps. They get a large pile. They run off to the stream.*

Scene 10

Bridge over stream. TYKE *and* DANNY *approach bridge and ceremoniously toss the leaflets into the water.*

TYKE: I hope the fish like rents and rates.

DANNY: Might be eaten by a shark.

TYKE: It'll get belly-ache, then.

TYKE *and* DANNY *throw stones at the disappearing leaflets.*

TYKE: We'll see who wins this election.

MUSIC

EPISODE THREE

Keeping Track

1 The children in the class clearly enjoy the story of the seige which Sir tells them. Which aspects of the story particularly interest them?

2 There is a brief appearance by a tramp in this episode. It might be said that the writer uses *irony* again at this point. (Look back at the question at the end of Episode One.) How is the author being 'ironic' in this brief mention of the tramp?

3 In Tyke's home there is talk of canvassing for the local election. What is canvassing?

4 Do you see any difference between the way Tyke and Kneeshaw feel about the local election?

5 What happens to the leaflets Tyke and Danny are delivering?

6 Describe Danny's reactions towards the deserted building.

7 What does Tyke think the room they discover might be used for?

8 The story (or plot) concerning the theft was dealt with in Episodes One and Two. This episode is introducing new story or plot lines. What are they? (Can you find at least *two* elements in the plot of Episode Three which are likely to be continued in subsequent episodes?)

A Closer Look

1 Why do you think the den in the deserted mill is an interesting idea to Tyke? What does Tyke say it might be used for?

2 Why do children like to have dens? Give examples of different kinds of dens – perhaps draw some plans – and say how they are used.

3 The information you collect about dens might be displayed. Include drawings, clear information on how to construct a den (the materials needed) and how to fit it out to make it habitable.

Explorations

On the way home from their day out the children chant a rhyme. How many rhymes of this do you know? It might be interesting to attempt a collection.

Write down the rhymes you know.

Ask your friends in other classes to add more.

Talk to your parents and grandparents to find if they remember any such rhymes from when they were young.

Put all the rhymes you have collected together in a class book. (If you have kept to rhymes which have been chanted or sung in your local area − that is, not used rhymes from books − you might consider publishing the collection to sell to people in the community. The funds you collect might then be used for a charity or for some project you have under way in school.)

EPISODE FOUR

Scene 1
School corridor outside 4M's classroom. 4M charge down the corridor and into their classroom.

Scene 2
4M's classroom in school. 4M are charging in but come to an abrupt and awesome hush. Waiting for them at the top of the class are SIR, and a glamorous young woman. SIR is beaming. The kids sidle their way to their tables.

SIR: Right. I'd like to introduce you to Miss Honeywell. She will be taking the class for the next five weeks. Some of the time I won't be here so I want you to be very good. Well? Aren't you going to welcome her?

SEVERAL VOICES: Welcome, Miss Honeywell.

MISS HONEYWELL *(in a very posh accent)*: It's absolutely splendid to meet you all. Please call me Jenny.

DANNY: *(savouring the name quietly)*: Jenny.

SIR: Actually, I think they'll call you Miss. They usually do. Now I expect you'd like to meet them. Carry on with the work in your folders, children, while Jenny – er – Miss Honeywell comes around to talk to you.

KNEESHAW: Me, Miss.

LINDA: No, me first.

KEVIN SIMES: Me, please, Miss.

SIR: Quiet!

MISS HONEYWELL *approaches* TYKE *and* DANNY'*s desks.*

MISS HONEYWELL *(to* DANNY*)*: What are you drawing?

DANNY *(unclearly)*: That's a drawing of Tyke and me finding a skellinton.

MISS HONEYWELL *(very polite)*: Oh.

TYKE: He's saying that it's a drawing of him and me finding a skeleton.

MISS HONEYWELL: Oh, how very interesting! What sort of skeleton?

TYKE: A sheep's.

MISS HONEYWELL: Oh. Splendid. What's your name?

TYKE: Tyke Tiler.

MISS HONEYWELL: No, your real name?

TYKE *(worried)*: No, but no one calls me anything else. Not ever.

MISS HONEYWELL: I see, Tyke.

TYKE *is obviously relieved.* MISS HONEYWELL *turns to go to another table.*

TYKE *(quietly to* DANNY*)*: She's going to be all right.

Scene 3
Looking down school stairs from top. SIR *and* IAN PITT *are walking up stairs.*

PITT: She's a student, Sir, isn't she?

SIR *smiles.*

PITT: Why do we have to have students, Sir?

SIR: They have to practise, don't they? How else would they learn how to teach?

PITT: But why do they have to practise on us? *They* can't keep us quiet and then *we* get into trouble.

Scene 4
4M's classroom in school. The HEAD *is addressing the class.* MISS HONEYWELL *is looking on.*

HEAD: I'm very sorry, Miss Honeywell, to introduce
unpleasantness on your first day at Cricklepit, but we have
discovered that the schoolkeeper's garden has been vandalised.
The garden planted by Mr Steggles and the class of 2M has been
wrecked. And all the fish have been thrown out of the pond on
to the bank where they have suffocated. So, you can imagine
how the children of 2M feel about that.

DANNY: They don't feel very happy, Sir?

HEAD: Quite right, Danny, thank you. What I am here to say,
and to all the classes in the school, is that if the culprits are not
found then the pupils as a whole will lose certain privileges. So I
am asking each of you to exert whatever pressure you can to
ensure the guilty person, or persons, come forward. Thank you,
Miss Honeywell.

> HEAD *gives a big beam and departs.*

DANNY *(privately to* TYKE*)*: What's he mean?

TYKE: He means we shall all suffer unless somebody owns up.

LINDA: Please, Miss.

MISS HONEYWELL: Yes.

LINDA: Please, Miss. I think it was awful to kill all those fish and
just leave them on the ground to die.

MISS HONEYWELL: I certainly agree, Linda.

LINDA: And, Miss. I bet it was Sandra Hines in 4P . . .

> *The* CLASS *groans in rejection of this.*

PITT: Just because you hate her. You're jealous of her.

TYKE: She pinched your little boyfriend, didn't she?

KNEESHAW: It seems to me, Miss, that it must've been done by
someone a bit thick, someone not too bright. Now, Danny
Price is not right in the head, he's right round the twist. I bet it
was him, Miss.

PITT: Danny's worth ten of you, you squinting thug.

> TYKE *leaps onto* KNEESHAW*,* SIMES *joins in,* DANNY
> *tugs at Simes.* EVERYONE *is milling around.*

MISS HONEYWELL: Stop it. Stop it. Stop it!

> *Door opens and in walk the* HEAD *and* MRS SOMERS. KNEESHAW's *nose is bleeding.*

MRS SOMERS: Really, Miss Honeywell, what is that child doing?

HEAD *(icily)*: Be absolutely still, all of you. *(to* TYKE*)* I'll see you in my office directly after break. Kneeshaw, stop bleeding with such wild enthusiasm. Sit up and get your head back. When you are quite recovered I shall want to see you too, Martin. What is it, Danny?

DANNY *(unclearly)*: Tyke hit him because he said I did it.

MRS SOMERS: Really!

HEAD: Really? In fact, I've just had a phone call from the Head of St Philip's. It appears four big boys from there were seen by a neighbour leaving our grounds this morning. It seems they are the culprits. But that doesn't excuse this outbreak. I'll see you later, Danny, as well. I will deal with all of you in turn.

> *A glance at* MISS HONEYWELL *and* HEAD *leaves followed by* MRS SOMERS.

MISS HONEYWELL: Oh dear. *(sighs.)*

Scene 5

School corridor outside HEAD's *office.* TYKE *is waiting fearfully. Several voices can be heard coming from downstairs.* TYKE *moves closer to listen. The* HEAD, SIR, *and* MRS SOMERS *are in discussion.*

MRS SOMERS: I'll say it once more. That pair are trouble makers. We won't have any peace until they are separated.

SIR: I can't agree. It's wrong to separate friends.

> TYKE *moves up to top of stairs to see who's talking.*

Scene 6

At the foot of the school stairs. The HEAD, MRS SOMERS, SIR *are in discussion.*

MRS SOMERS: I know it well from teaching them last year. That child Tiler is a nuisance.

SIR: Tyke is the only stable influence in that boy's life. Look at his background. That awful mother; father gone who knows where . . .

HEAD: Prison.

MRS SOMERS: You see. Danny Price must be sent to the Russell Dene school where they have facilities to deal with children of that type.

HEAD: They'll be doing their tests next week. If Danny does well in the test he will go to the Comprehensive with Tyke. If he does badly in the test we may have to consider a special school. The verbal reasoning test will tell us all we need to know.

Scene 7

School corridor outside Head's office TYKE *is listening anxiously. Comes to a decision and moves back to the Head's door which is open.*

MRS SOMERS: I would be happier if we could get in touch with the Education Welfare Officer now and start a review of Danny's case. I think we might also need to contact the authority's Psychologist . . .

After some hesitation TYKE *enters the Head's office.*

Scene 8

The Head's office. TYKE *slips in and approaches the Head's desk. On top there is a polythene folder with papers in.* TYKE *slips one out of the folder, scans it earnestly, folds it in four, and leaves. We see that the papers on the desk are headed 'Verbal Reasoning Tests'.*

MUSIC

EPISODE FOUR

Keeping Track

1 How do you know that Miss Honeywell is an inexperienced teacher at the beginning of this episode?

2 Do you think she is going to be all right? What evidence do you have for thinking this?

3 What does Pitt say about students? Do you agree?

4 What has happened to 2M's garden?

5 What does Linda have to say about this? Why does she say what she says? Is this the first time Linda has tried to get someone into trouble?

6 Why does Kneeshaw assume it must have been Danny who damaged the garden? How does Tyke react to this?

7 What does Tyke overhear? How much more do you learn about Danny from this overheard conversation?

8 What differences do you see between Mrs Somers and Sir (Mr Merchant) in their view of Danny?

9 What does Tyke do as a result of the overheard conversation?

10 What do you think is going to happen?

A Closer Look

1 Write a plan for Episode Five predicting what you think might happen as a result of the events you have just read in Episode Four.

2 Write *two* reports on Danny:
   (a) from Mr Merchant,
   (b) from Mrs Somers.

At the end of the reports say what you think ought to happen to Danny in the future.

3 Write a letter from Miss Honeywell to her mother in which she tells her mother what 4M are like and what sort of impression she thinks she has made on them.

Explorations

1 Write a story called, 'The Overheard Conversation'.
2 Act out or write a scene in which an experienced teacher gives advice to a new teacher about how to handle a difficult class.

EPISODE FIVE

Scene 1

Beryl's bedroom in Tyke's home. Pop music is playing loudly on a cassette player.
BERYL is making herself up in front of her mirror. There's a knock on the door. TYKE enters.

BERYL: I didn't say 'Come in'.

TYKE: Sorry. Turn it down, Berry. Please.

BERYL: What's the matter and get on with it, 'cos I'm going canvassing with Richard.

TYKE: Please help me with this. Check the answers for me.

> BERYL *turns, reads the test paper, is shocked, turns down volume of tape.*

BERYL: Tyke, that's cheating. You know what Dad would say about anything like this. Take it back quick before you get into trouble.

TYKE: I'm not cheating. I'm doing this for Danny, not me. If he can't get a bit of a score on this, he'll have to go to another school and he can't manage without me. And he'll miss his other mates as well.

BERYL: Are you sure?

TYKE: 'Cross my heart and hope to die,
    Drop down dead if I tell a lie.'

> BERYL *sighs.*

BERYL: OK. But we mustn't let anyone know, or all hell will break out.

44

TYKE *(simply)*: Thanks, Berry.

BERYL *(reading)*: 'Write the word which has both of these meanings: (a) a place of worship; (b) part of the side of the head.'

Scene 2

TYKE's *bedroom.* TYKE *is coaching* DANNY.

TYKE: (a) a place of worship; (b) part of the side of the head.

DANNY: I can't do these, Tyke.

TYKE: Temple, temple. A temple is a place where you worship in. And this is your temple. *(gestures)*

DANNY: Temple.

TYKE: Remember it. 'If 246153 means *"enfold"* then 614352 means ... ?' What does it mean, Danny?

Scene 3

The 'secret room' in the mill. TYKE *and* DANNY *are talking.*

TYKE: 614352?

DANNY: Can we go home now, Tyke?

TYKE: Look, 246153 is e, n, f, o, l, d, so 614352 is ... OK. Forget it. When you see the question beginning '246 ...', the answer is 'fondle'.

DANNY: Fondle. What have we got all this stuff for, Tyke?

DANNY *indicates beside them the supplies which* TYKE *has brought: tin of Elastoplast: a packet of cream crackers, half a jar of jam, a tin opener, a tin of beans, a spoon, two paperbacks and some comics.*

TYKE: So as we're set up. This could be our secret hideout. We could come here if we were in a siege. That's why I've got the provisions. You've gotta have provisions for a siege.

DANNY: I don't like it here. There are ghosties in this place.

TYKE: Oh, shurrup. Back to the test. *(passes over two sweets.)*

Scene 4

TYKE's *bedroom.* TYKE *is still coaching* DANNY.

TYKE: 'If 246153 means *"enfold"* then 614352 means ... ?'

   Pause.

TYKE: *Fondle, Fondle*!! When you see 246 ... the answer is *fondle*.
DANNY: Can't we watch telly now, Tyke?
TYKE: No, we can't. I'll tell you one thing, Danny Price. I'm
   never, never going to be a teacher. No, thank you. 'Write the
   word which has both these meanings: (a) a place of worship; (b)
   part of the side of your head.'
DANNY: Temple!
TYKE: Well done!

   TYKE *hands over two sweets as reward.*

Scene 5

4M's *classroom in school.* MISS HONEYWELL *is teaching. There's
massive evidence of a project on King Arthur. A huge romantic
Arthurian mural has been done by the kids.*

MISS HONEYWELL: Now here's my plan: we're going to do a
   play about King Arthur for the end of term and bring all these
   characters to life.

   MISS HONEYWELL *indicates mural.* SIR *enters.*

SIR: Excuse me interrupting, Miss Honeywell, but you said you
   had some classwork to show me.
MISS HONEYWELL: Yes, Mr Merchant, I thought you'd like to
   see our mural. Isn't it splendid?
SIR: Very fine. Very good work, indeed.

   SIR *turns to the class.*

SIR: Of course, it wasn't really like that at all.

KNEESHAW: Wasn't it, Sir?
TYKE: No, Sir?

MISS HONEYWELL *is not at all pleased.*

SIR: No. You see, the real King Arthur was one of those who defended Britain after the collapse of the Roman Empire. All those castles and romantic armour were made up by the poets and writers later. I bet Arthur and his knights didn't have a spare moment to go around rescuing damsels in distress.
MISS HONEYWELL *(very cool)*: Thank you, Mr Merchant. Now get on with the work in your folders, children.

The CLASS *goes on working.* SIR *approaches* MISS HONEYWELL, *grinning.*

SIR: I don't like to get too far from the facts.
MISS HONEYWELL: Facts! Ideas and imagination are what matter.

SIR *then drops his voice but this only increases the attention of the* CLASS.

SIR: Have a meal with me tonight and we can argue it out.

MISS HONEYWELL *is non-committal.*

SIR: I know a very good Italian place near the station. See you after school and we can fix it up.

MISS HONEYWELL *scarcely reacts. The* CLASS *can hardly hide their glee.*

Scene 6
School playground. On a school wall we see a hand written message:
BILL LOVES JENNY. *Another hand is writing a speech bubble:* I
LOVE YOU, JENNY. *The speech bubble is part of a portrait of a man and woman done by a twelve-year-old artist. Another chalk written sign* KISS ME BILL. *Hand splashes wet cloth over chalk graffiti.*

Scene 7

School playground. SIR is watching severely over a cleaning-up operation. 4M are cleaning up the graffiti with buckets and old rags. TYKE is on tip-toe on a chair stretching up to clean a comment almost beyond reach. KNEESHAW is below cleaning another.

SIR: Come on, Kneeshaw, I want every trace of writing and chalk off that wall.

KNEESHAW: It's not fair, Sir. I didn't do any of this.

    TYKE *loses control of the basin of water and it tilts to release a full stream of dirty soapy water over* KNEESHAW.

SIR: I've had enough from you this time, Tyke.

Scene 8

Head's study in school. TYKE is once more standing before the HEAD who is watering his plant with the tea-pot.

HEAD: You have been here too often, this term, Tyke. What are we going to do with you this time, eh?

TYKE: I don't know, Sir.

HEAD: I have it. Every playtime, dinner time and for twenty minutes after school for the next week, you will go to Mrs Somers and help her in any way she needs. Now, go. I don't want to see you again this term.

TYKE *(miserable)*: Thank you, Sir.

HEAD: And get a good night's sleep, you have that Verbal Reasoning Test tomorrow.

Scene 9

School stairs. 4M are coming up in pairs. TYKE and DANNY are last and talking sotto voce.

TYKE: When you see 246 . . . ?
DANNY: It's fondle.

Episode Five

TYKE: Place of worship and side of head.
DANNY: Temple.
TYKE: Sheep is to lamb as goat is to ... ?
DANNY: Kid.

They have come to the door of the hall. Outside 4M's *classroom* SIR *is handing out the tests.* MISS HONEYWELL *is handing out new pencils.*

SIR *(to each group)*: Don't open the paper until I tell you to. Read the instructions carefully.

MISS HONEYWELL *stops* DANNY *and speaks with well-meaning concern.*

MISS HONEYWELL: Now, Danny, you mustn't worry. You just do your best.
DANNY: Yes, Miss.
TYKE: *(with a reassuring smile)*: I think he's going to be alright, Miss.

MUSIC

EPISODE FIVE

Keeping Track

1 What are Tyke's reasons for planning to cheat in the test?
2 How does Tyke teach Danny the answers in the test?
3 Is this a difficult task Tyke has undertaken?
4 How does the writer show us that the teaching of Danny takes a
  long time?
5 Why are 4M pleased that Mr Merchant has asked Miss Honeywell
  out to dinner?

A Closer Look

1 It is clear that by the end of this episode Tyke is beginning to have
  some success with teaching Danny. It is also clear from earlier
  episodes that Danny's teachers have *not* had much success with
  teaching Danny – some of them cannot even understand what
  Danny is saying. Discuss *why* you think Tyke is able to achieve
  what the teachers have failed to achieve.
2 Is Tyke right to help Danny in this way? Is he helping Danny
  really? Write or act a scene in which you talk to Tyke about this
  issue. Do you encourage Tyke to go on with the plan to help
  Danny cheat, or do you try to talk Tyke out of it?

Explorations

Have you ever had an important test in school? If so, what was it?
What happened? How did you prepare for it? How did you feel
before and during the test? How did your friends appear to be

feeling? What was the atmosphere like in the room where you did the test? Did your parents say very much to you about what they expected of you? Did this help?

When you have discussed this as a class get together in groups to prepare a list of advice items which you might give to children (and their parents, and teachers) on 'How to Cope with the Important Test or Examination'. You might consider the following headings as a guide to your discussion and final piece of writing:

What is the best way to prepare?

How can you be helped by parents and teachers?

What advice would you give to someone who gets very nervous before tests?

Do you have any advice to give on how to react when you are given the results of the test?

EPISODE SIX

Scene 1
4M's classroom at school. MISS HONEYWELL *is setting up the end of term play.* TYKE *is reading from* The Sword in the Stone *by T. H. White.*

TYKE: Miss, what we've sorted out is that Ian will be King Arthur, Lorraine will be Guinevere, Martin Kneeshaw will be Lancelot, Linda will play Morgan le Fay and Danny will be Sir Galahad.

MISS HONEYWELL: Absolutely super. I think you will all be splendid. And, Danny, remember that Galahad's strength was as the strength of ten because his heart was pure. I think that's like you.

    DANNY *is pleased but embarrassed. Several 'yuk' sounds from others in the* CLASS.

DANNY: *(to himself)*: 'My strength is as the strength of ten.
                     My strength is as the strength of ten.'

    MISS HONEYWELL *approaches* TYKE *and speaks quietly.*

MISS HONEYWELL: Tyke, will you tell your Daddy that I'll come around tonight in case there's anything I can do to help for the election tomorrow.

Scene 2
Outside TYKE's *house, which is decorated with election posters:* VOTE FOR EDWARD TILER *and* COMMITTEE ROOMS. MISS

Episode Six

HONEYWELL *is ringing the doorbell.* DAD *answers. His face is appreciative.*

DAD: You must be Miss Honeywell.
MISS HONEYWELL: Call me Jenny, please.
DAD: Well, Jenny, nice of you to join us on our kamikaze trip. Come in, we've a lot of leaflets and polling lists to sort out.

DAD's *way back to the house is blocked by* TYKE *and* DANNY *squeezing out, loaded with posters.*

TYKE: Hello, Miss.
DANNY: Hello, Miss.
TYKE: Sorry we can't wait. Got to do some posters.

MISS HONEYWELL *goes in leaving* DAD *talking to* TYKE.

DAD: And be polite to people. Even some of my supporters don't want my poster up in their window. Don't be too pushy.

Scene 3
Street near TYKE's *house.* DANNY *and* TYKE *are rushing along.*

TYKE: Did you say something about supporters, Danny? I said nothing about supporters. Now what number was Kneeshaw's house?
DANNY: I don't know, Tyke. He'd never let me come round to his house.
TYKE: Anyway, we'll know by the posters.

Scene 4
KNEESHAW's *house, which is even more covered in posters than* TYKE's. VOTE FOR GRENDON KNEESHAW *is on all the windows, in the hedge, on the gate.*
Silently TYKE *and* DANNY *set about pasting* VOTE FOR TILER *over as many* KNEESHAW *posters as they can reach. They plaster an extra two for luck on the front door and escape.*

Scene 5

The living room of TYKE's *home. It is election day. Leaflets, poll lists everywhere.* TYKE *and* DANNY *are on a sofa reading comics.* DAD *is on the phone.*

DAD: Yesterday evening, you think? . . . Well, I can assure you that I know nothing about it, Mr Kneeshaw. Nothing whatsoever. I can't imagine who would think of doing such a thing . . . *(As he speaks he turns and looks meaningfully at* TYKE *and* DANNY.) Well, . . . I'm sure you will do exactly what you think is right . . . Goodbye to you, Mr Kneeshaw. *(He puts the phone down.)*

Silence.

DAD: Tiler posters on Kneeshaw's house. Know anything about it?

DANNY: Yes, we did it, Mr Tiler.

TYKE *kicks* DANNY's *foot, too late.*

DANNY: I like you, Mr Tiler.

TYKE: What did he say, Dad?

DAD: He says that when he's elected he's going to bring up a complaint about it. *(pause, he grins)* So I can't think we have much to worry about. Now it's time to run down and get another set of tally cards from the polling station.

TYKE: I feel lousy, I've got a headache.

DANNY: Come on, Tyke. It doesn't take long.

TYKE *and* DANNY *get up to leave.*

DAD: And stay away from the Kneeshaws.

Scene 6

Street near TYKE's *house.* TYKE *and* DANNY *are walking towards the school. For once,* DANNY *is in front of* TYKE.

DANNY: Haven't seen Martin yet. I thought he was running for his Dad.

TYKE: Huh.
DANNY: What's up?
TYKE: The sky.
DANNY: Gee, Tyke, you're in a rotten mood.
TYKE: I feel bad. Now leave me alone.
DANNY: If you feel like that . . .
TYKE: Yes, I do.
DANNY: OK. You can do it on your own then.
TYKE: I couldn't care less.

> MARTIN KNEESHAW *comes quietly around the corner and trips* TYKE *up.* TYKE *curls up and gets another kick in the back.*

KNEESHAW: That's for mucking up our house.

> KEVIN SIMMS, *who is there too, laughs.* TYKE *can't get up, and has to struggle against dizziness.* KNEESHAW *looms overhead, threatening and distorted.*

KNEESHAW: My Dad'll beat your'n. You wait and see.

> KNEESHAW's *image swirls and disappears. Street, lamp-posts, sky, all merge into confusion.*

TYKE: Danny? Danny Price? Where are you?

> *Darkness falls.* DANNY *has returned with* DAD *and* MISS HONEYWELL.

DAD: Tyke, are you all right?
MISS HONEYWELL: What happened, Tyke?
DANNY: You're drunk. I could see you was ill so I fetched 'em.

> *Their three faces swirl into blackness again.*

Scene 7
TYKE's *bedroom.* TYKE *is in bed, eyes closed, very weak.* MUM *is by the bedside.* TYKE *comes to.*

TYKE: What happened?

MUM: You passed out. You've got a virus infection. You'll be all right now.

TYKE: Who won?

MUM: Dad won, of course.

TYKE *relaxes and smiles.*

TYKE: Where's Danny? Can he come and see me?

MUM: Yes, sure. But not yet. You've been quite ill and it will be a couple of weeks before you are fully recovered. Now go to sleep.

MUM *kisses* TYKE *on the forehead.* TYKE *settles back to sleep.*

Scene 8

TYKE's *bedroom a week or so later. A cassette player is playing light pop.* TYKE *is sitting in bed with a dressing-gown on, reading* The Sword in the Stone *and obviously recovering. Voices float up from downstairs.* TYKE *stops reading, gets up and leaves the room.*

Scene 9

The stairs and hall of TYKE's *home.* TYKE *is creeping secretly down the stairs.* MUM *is listening to the* HEAD *in the living room. Gradually the voices become clearer as* TYKE *stops by the half-open living room door, the last sentences are crystal clear.*

HEAD: The test results show that Tyke has exceptional ability and we must plan carefully for the future. You know it has always been a pleasure to teach your children, Mrs Tiler. We didn't have much faith in Tyke but it seems it may have been because Tyke was a late developer. Not uncommon in a third child you know. We were worried about mixing with unsuitable companions but, as it turns out – and these Verbal Reasoning Tests are very important . . .

Episode Six

Scene 10
TYKE's *living room.*

HEAD: ... Tyke has proved to be very much above average. We must do everything possible to encourage such a mind.

TYKE *enters.* MUM *and* HEAD *look up, smiling.*

MUM: Don't look so worried, dear. Come and sit. Your Head Teacher had just told me that you've done exceptionally well in the test. The highest possible, in fact.

HEAD: I must admit that I was surprised, but there is no doubt about it. Your test results were without a single mistake.

MUM: Tyke, close your mouth, dear. You look stupid like that and we know you aren't, don't we?

HEAD: To come to the point, we should like you to apply for a place at the Dorrington School for gifted children. Would you like that?

TYKE: What about Danny in the test?

HEAD: Danny? Oh, yes. He did quite well and will go to Dawson Comprehensive with the others. But don't worry, I'm sure that with the wonderful range of opportunity presented to you at Dorrington, you will have no time to miss your friends, and will soon make fresh ones, eh?

MUM: I must say that it's come as a delightful surprise. Tyke never seemed to take any interest in academic subjects.

HEAD *(rising)*: Well, Mrs Tiler, I must be on my way. Good-bye, child. Glad to see you're so much better. *(leaves followed by* MUM*)* I look forward to talking to Tyke's father too, when he's back.

TYKE *sits dejected and alone on the sofa.*

TYKE *(thinking)*: It's all gone wrong again. How am I going to get out of this? I don't want to go to that school!

EPISODE SIX

Keeping Track

1 'Well, Jenny, nice of you to join us on our kamikaze trip' says Tyke's Dad. What does 'kamikaze' mean? Why does Mr Tiler call the election campaign that?
2 How do Tyke and Danny try to 'help' in the campaign?
3 Who tells Mr Tiler what Tyke and Danny have done? Why does that person tell?
4 What does Tyke's Dad mean by 'cornered animals are dangerous'?
5 Why does Danny assume that Tyke is drunk? What is the matter with Tyke?
6 How does Tyke's illness help the author to move the story along more quickly?
7 Do the test results upset Tyke's plans? How?

A Closer Look

Look closely at the words Danny keeps saying from the play: 'My strength is as the strength of ten' etc. At first this repeated phrase is funny? Can you say why?

As Danny keeps repeating the phrase it becomes clear that the author is using it to emphasise something else about Danny. What do you think that something is?

As you read the rest of the play take particular notice of how this phrase is used.

Explorations

Write a story about an illness (or an accident). Explain how it came about. Say how you felt. What was it like being confined to bed and/ or your house? Did the people around you treat you differently? Did the illness change you in any way? Did it change the way you saw other people?

EPISODE 7

Scene 1

The living room of Tyke's house. MUM *is getting ready to go out, marching up and down, trying to put on her coat, umbrella flailing.* DAD *is standing by helpless.*

MUM: I shall go. I shan't stay here where I'm not wanted and where nobody, nobody takes the least notice of what I say . . .

DAD: Put down that umbrella, Mary, you'll hit something.

    TYKE *enters with* CRUMBLE.

MUM: For all the notice any of you take, I might just as well be invisible.

DAD *(weary)*: Oh, don't go on.

MUM: You can talk. All you care about are committees and poking your nose in other people's business. I'm the last to get any consideration. Tyke has this wonderful chance to go to a special school for gifted children and you want to stand in her way. *(to Tyke)* You've been in trouble from one end of this term to the other, you and that Danny Price.

DAD: Tyke's all right . . .

MUM: Tyke! Tyke! How I hate that name! And that's your fault too. I chose a perfectly good name and you had to make such a joke of it . . .

TYKE: If you're starting in about names, I'm off.

    TYKE *starts to leave.*

MUM: Here, don't forget your sick-note.

Episode Seven

MUM *takes note from table and gives it to Tyke then speaks more softly to Tyke.*

MUM: Have a good day at school.

TYKE *leaves.*

MUM: *(sharply to Dad)*: You see, *I* have to think of everything.

Scene 2
The school playground. TYKE *is approached by* LINDA, IAN, KNEESHAW, KEVIN *and others in* 4M.

LINDA: Where is he?
IAN: Did he go to your house?
KEVIN: They've got the police in.
KNEESHAW: You must know where he is.
LINDA: His Mum was 'ere.
TYKE: Hey! What's it all about? What are you talking about?

Silence.

KNEESHAW: Well, Well, Well. So Tyke doesn't know. Well I'll tell you, with great pleasure. Your kleptomaniac friend, Danny Price, has struck again. And this time he's pinched Mrs Somers' –gold watch and the police have been here. And Danny's run away.

TYKE *dismisses Kneeshaw with a snort and goes right past him, brushing him aside.*

Scene 3
At the front gates of the school. TYKE *comes out and purposefully walks away.*

Scene 4
Mill exterior. TYKE *approaches mill and goes in.*

Scene 5

The 'secret room' in the mill. DANNY *is there, curled up behind the boxes.* TYKE *enters.*

TYKE *(very softly)*: Danny.

DANNY *(turning round, angry)*: You've bin a long time. You took your time getting here. I'd've thought you'd've known where I'd gone and come and joined me. Lonely it was. Blooming lonely, without you and with only Fatty to keep all them ghosties away.

TYKE: I got here as quickly as I could, Danny.

DANNY: You've gotter tell 'em I didn't do it. I didn't take it, Tyke, honest. Martin Kneeshaw and Kevin Simms took that watch and put it in my bag to get their own back on me. They bin on at me all the time while you bin away.

TYKE: I couldn't help it. I was ill in bed.

DANNY *(very sorry for himself)*: Well you gotter sort it out now.

TYKE: Yeah, but how to do it, eh?

DANNY: I tell you how to do it. Capture Martin Kneebags and Kevin Slimy and torture 'em till they tell the truth.

TYKE: What do we do to 'em?

DANNY: Oh, tie 'em up and . . . hit 'em . . . and you know, torture 'em . . . like on the telly.

TYKE: Don't be stupid.

DANNY: I thought you'd help me.

TYKE: Yeh.

DANNY: Then do somethin'.

  TYKE *gets up to go.*

TYKE: I'll think of something. Don't worry, Danny.

DANNY: Sort 'em out . . . duff 'em in. Only don't be long, Tyke. I don't like it here with ghosties.

  TYKE: *stares back at Danny, thinking very hard. Pause.*

TYKE: I know exactly what to do. See you soon, Danny.

TYKE *leaves.*

Scene 6

Corridor outside the Head's door in the school. TYKE *walks up to Head's door, stares at it, looks around, finally knocks.*

HEAD: Come in.

TYKE *opens door and enters.*

Scene 7

The Head's office. The HEAD *is once more watering his plant.*

HEAD: It requires a remarkable amount of liquid refreshment. (*He sits and looks up at* TYKE.)

HEAD: Have you come to give your excuses, ill-founded or otherwise, for absenting yourself from this establishment without permission?

TYKE: I've come to strike a bargain, Sir.

Silence.

HEAD (*coldly*): Is it customary for pupils to strike bargains with their headteachers?

TYKE (*fast*): I know where he is, Danny, my friend, and I can take you to him if you get the truth out of Martin Kneeshaw and Kevin Simms, because they did it, they took the watch, not Danny, and he's not stolen anything since Miss Honeywell said his strength was as the strength of ten, like Sir Galahad . . .

HEAD: And where do our young friends, Martin and Kevin, enter into this?

TYKE: They don't like me and they've been getting at Danny.

HEAD: Getting at?

TYKE: Oh, you know . . . laughing at him and fighting him and tormenting him while I've been away and not able to look after him, and I know they took the watch because it was Kevin Simms found it in his shoebag ...

HEAD: Martin Kneeshaw is a helpful boy and Kevin Simms is rarely in trouble, whereas you and Danny Price have been among my most frequent visitors. Who am I to believe?

TYKE: Me, oh, me. They're creeps.

HEAD: I think we had better stop wasting time. Take me to Danny Price.

TYKE: Sir, please believe me. Please send for them and make them tell the truth. You can do it. You're the Head, and you said ... I wasn't much given ... to mend ... mendacity.

  Silence.

TYKE: Telling lies, Sir.

HEAD *(very quietly)*: I know what it means.

  Silence.

HEAD: *(at last)*: I believe you, Tyke. Go back to your class and send Kneeshaw and Simms to me. I'll deal with them. I'll ask Mr Merchant to go with you to find Danny.

TYKE *(mightily relieved and grinning)*: Thank you, Sir.

Scene 8

The 'secret room' in the mill. DANNY is curled up on old sacks fast asleep. Footsteps approach.

SIR: Heavens above!

  TYKE *approaches DANNY and shakes him awake.*

TYKE: Danny?

DANNY: I'm glad you've come, Tyke. Hello, Sir. I didn't want to spend another night with the ghosties. Did you beat them in for me? Kneeshaw and Simms? Did you torture them?

SIR: Yes, Danny, something like that.

TYKE: We didn't do the torturing personally. We got someone else to do it.

SIR: Right, let's get you two home. There are a lot of people waiting to be nice to you.

Scene 9

The kitchen of Tyke's house, TYKE *enters to find* MUM *and* DAD *hugging.*

TYKE: Oh, have you two made it up, then?

No reaction.

TYKE: I'm glad you're not rowing any more but there's no need to go that far.

Eventually MUM *and* DAD *separate. They grin.*

TYKE: Well, what's the verdict? Do I have to go to that rotten special school or not?

MUM: No, dear. We're sure you'll be best off with your friends.

TYKE: Thanks, Mum. Thanks, Dad.

MUSIC

EPISODE SEVEN

Keeping Track

1 What has happened to Danny whilst Tyke is ill?
2 Why has Danny run away? Where has he gone?
3 What does Danny see as the solution to his problems? (What does he want Tyke to do?)
4 What is Tyke's method of solving Danny's problem?
5 At the beginning of the episode Tyke's mother and father are in the middle of an argument. The reason for the argument is not explained until the end of the episode. What has it been about?

A Closer Look

1 Write or act the scene in which Kneeshaw and Kevin Simms are interviewed by the Head. Why have they stolen the watch and tried to get Danny into trouble?
2 Act or write an interview with Tyke about why telling the Head about Kneeshaw and Simms was the best thing. You might also try to discover how Tyke has changed from the beginning of the story – and why?

EPISODE EIGHT

Scene 1
The school hall. MISS HONEYWELL, TYKE and DANNY are arranging the props for the King Arthur play on a low platform at one end. Swords and helmets etc much in evidence.

MISS HONEYWELL: Danny, move that block a bit further forward or there will be no room for Ian to stand behind it.

    DANNY *does so,* TYKE *is carefully draping a coloured cloth over another block. They all stand back to check.*

MISS HONEYWELL: Well, here it is at last. The last day at Cricklepit School for all of us!
DANNY: Are you sorry to be leaving, Miss?
MISS HONEYWELL: I am, Danny. I've had a super time here.
TYKE: We should have something really special happening today. After all, I've been here eight years.
MISS HONEYWELL: Well, we do have our play. Come on! Let's get back to the classroom.

Scene 2
4M's classroom at school. Most of the class are grouped around Linda jostling to read the local newspaper which she is holding.

LINDA: Ger'off, it's mine.
IAN PITT: He'll be on telly now.

    MISS HONEYWELL *enters. Followed by* TYKE *and* DANNY.

LINDA: Have you seen this, Miss? It's about Sir's book on the school.

MISS HONEYWELL: Yes, I have seen it, Linda.

DANNY: Read it out, Tyke. Tell us what it says.

TYKE (*reading*): Mr William Merchant, who is a teacher at Cricklepit Combined School, has written a book on its history. It took him three years to research the story of the school's distant past.

IAN PITT: He didn't tell us, did he?

SIR *looks around the corner of the door.*

LINDA: Sir, you're goin' to be famous!

IAN PITT: You'll be on the telly, now. Won't you be, Sir?

SIR: I very much doubt it.

MISS HONEYWELL: I think you should be very proud of him, don't you?

LINDA: Oh we are, Miss!

TYKE (*still reading*): Thomas Tiler, caught climbing the school roof to ring the bell from the outside of the building, was whipped in front of the entire school and the managers.

IAN PITT: That must be one of your lot, Tyke!

DANNY: You'll be rich.

SIR: It's not exactly best-seller stuff, you know.

TYKE: Sir?

SIR: Yes, Tyke?

TYKE: When did they stop ringing the school bell?

SIR: During the war, when bells were only to be rung if the Germans invaded. Then part of the school was damaged by a bomb and it wasn't safe to ring the bell again, in case the bell tower had been weakened. By the way, Tyke, ask your father if it was a relation of yours that climbed up on the roof to ring it. But don't get any idea of doing it yourself, or you'll end up being whipped in front of the school and the managers.

Laughter.

SIR: Anyway, I didn't come in to talk about my book, but to thank Miss Honeywell for her work this term; and thank you 4M for your delightful company over the year and good luck in your new schools next term. Now the rest of the school are waiting eagerly for your performance of 'King Arthur'. Remember, sock it to 'em!

Cheers.

Scene 3

The school hall. 4M are performing. Their costumes rely mainly on headgear and props. TYKE is at the side of the stage reading.

TYKE: 'But now, farewell, I am going a long way . . .
　　　To the island-valley of Avilon
　　　Where falls not hail, or rain, or any snow
　　　Nor ever wind blows loudly; but it lies
　　　Deep-meadowed, happy, fair with orchard lawns
　　　And bowery hollows crowned with summer sea . . .'

4M have frozen into a final tableau. Pause. They turn awkwardly to the audience. Applause. The HEAD gets to his feet.

HEAD: Thank you 4M, and Miss Honeywell, for that elegiac evocation of our past. And now let us conclude the school year by giving thanks. We will sing 'When a knight won his spurs in the stories of old'.

The hymn begins. TYKE turns away and sidles out unnoticed.

Scene 4

The school playground and the bell tower. TYKE comes out of a door of the school and pauses, looks up at the bell-tower and moves closer. A quick scan of the building shows that climbing the tower is not impossible. We still hear the hymn from inside and during this scene we occasionally see Tyke's friends, enemies, teachers in full voice.

TYKE *starts to climb up to the bell. The hymn stops as* TYKE *gets close to the top and looks around at the city below, not noticing that people are coming out into the playground, pointing up:* DANNY, IAN PITT, KNEESHAW, SIMMS, LINDA, SIR, MISS HONEYWELL *are all there.*

DANNY: Tyke! Tyke! Come down. It's not safe.

The HEAD *elbows his way through them.*

HEAD: Just you come down, Tyke Tiler, and stop showing off so ostentatiously. It might prove disastrous.

Pause.

TYKE *(calling)*: All right, Sir.

MRS SOMERS *rounds a corner into the playground. Looks up at Tyke. Her face is red and corrugated with anger.*

MRS SOMERS: Get down at once, Theodora Tiler. Theodora Tiler, you naughty, disobedient girl.

TYKE *glares down with black rage. Moves back towards the bell.*

MRS SOMERS *(to the Head)*: What is that girl doing now?

TYKE *leans forward and swings the bell with all her might. It rings out loudly.*

SIR: Come down, Tyke, it's dangerous! Oh, no.

From the faces of the crowd and the sounds we hear we believe that something has given way and Tyke has slipped. DANNY *covers his face with his hands.*
Fade to black and silence.

Scene 5
Tyke's bedroom. Door opens, MUM *enters.* TYKE *is in bed, heavily bandaged and weak.*

MUM: Tyke. Mr Merchant has come to see you.

SIR *enters.*

SIR: Hello, Tyke.

MUM: She's got to be very quiet but something's worrying her
and she won't rest until she's told you herself.

MUM *leaves.*

TYKE *(weakly)*: Hello, Sir. I cheated. I didn't mean to. I had to
tell you.

SIR: What are you talking about?

TYKE: The test. I'm not clever. I did so well because I'd learnt all
the answers. I took the paper to help Danny. Then it all went
wrong.

SIR: Ah, the test. I did wonder about it at the time.

TYKE *(very meek)*: Will you tell Dad and the Head for me?

SIR *(laughing)*: Well, it hasn't made any difference in the long run,
so I should stop worrying. Go to sleep and concentrate on
getting better.

TYKE *slips down in the bed and closes her eyes.*

SIR: You've had quite a term of it.

TYKE: I have, haven't I?

A slight smile. She's asleep.

MUSIC

EPISODE EIGHT

Keeping Track

1 Why does Tyke climb the clocktower?
2 Is the discovery that Tyke is a girl a surprise to you?

A Closer Look

Why has the author not revealed that Tyke is a girl until the end?

AFTERWORDS

Looking At the Whole Story

1 Reports and Characters

In this section you are being asked to complete various sorts of reports on some of the characters in *The Turbulent Term of Tyke Tiler*. The reports are put together as questionnaires; to complete them you can use information from the play *and* information which you make up. The reports are set out in sections, each with a request for a particular sort of information. Write the heading down, then use as much space as you need to make your comments.

Report 1

To the County Education Department.
Name: *Daniel Price*.
Age:
Class:
Educational attainments:
Relationship with other children:
Relationship with adults:
Interests:
Physical health:
Learning difficulties:
Family background:
Behaviour:
Help already given in school:
Other comments:
Recommendations for future schooling:

Report 2
To Dorrington School:
Name: *Theodora Tiler*.
Age:
Class:
Position in class:
Special educational abilities:
Interests:
Relationship with other children:
Behaviour:
Attitude to school work:
Reasons why she is being recommended:
Other comments:

Report 3
To Cricklepit University, Teacher Training Department.
Name: *Jennifer Honeywell*:
Relationship with children:
Relationship with other staff:
Extra–curricula activities:
Other comments.

2 **Episode Nine**

Write an extra episode for the play which takes place two years after
Tyke and Danny leave Cricklepit Combined School. Are they still
friends? Have they changed? What is happening to them now? Is
Kneeshaw still their enemy? Has Tyke's attitude to being a girl
changed?

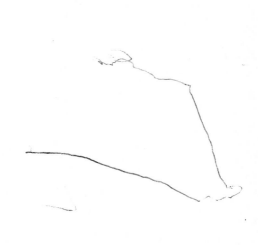